Stephen Duro

MORE FINGER JOGGING BOOGIE

17 pieces in lighter styles for piano

The Associated Board of
the Royal Schools of Music

MORE FINGER JOGGING BOOGIE

STEPHEN DURO

Southern Belle

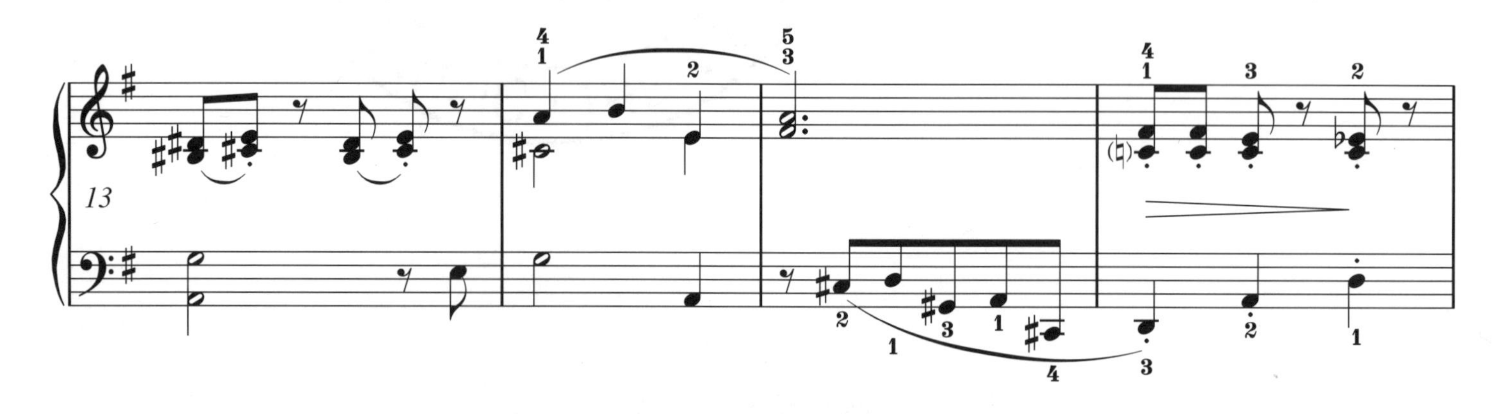

17
21
25
29
sub. p
33
mf
f
mp

Sam's Boogie

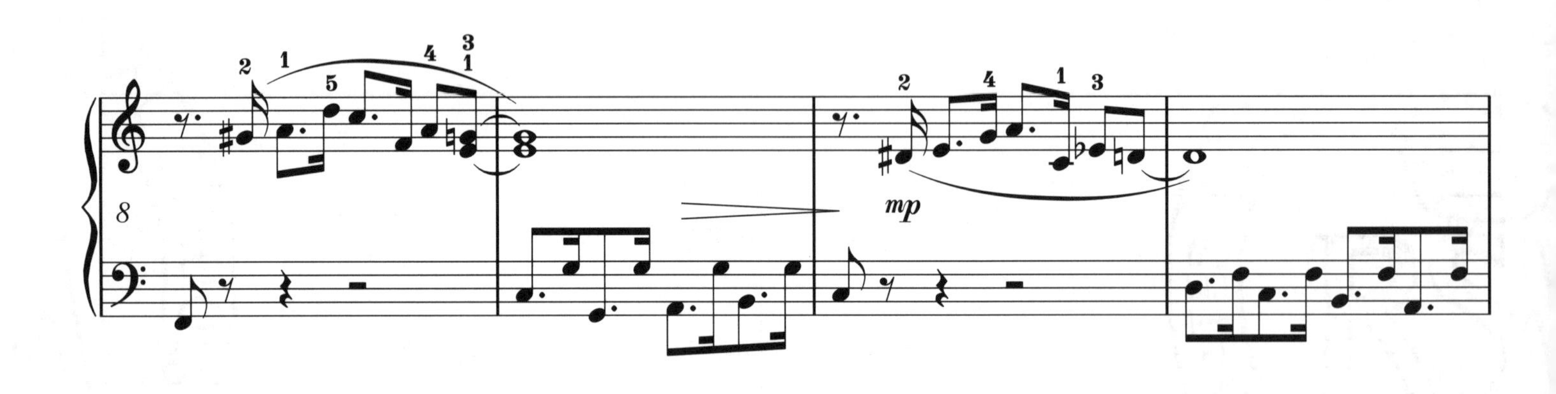

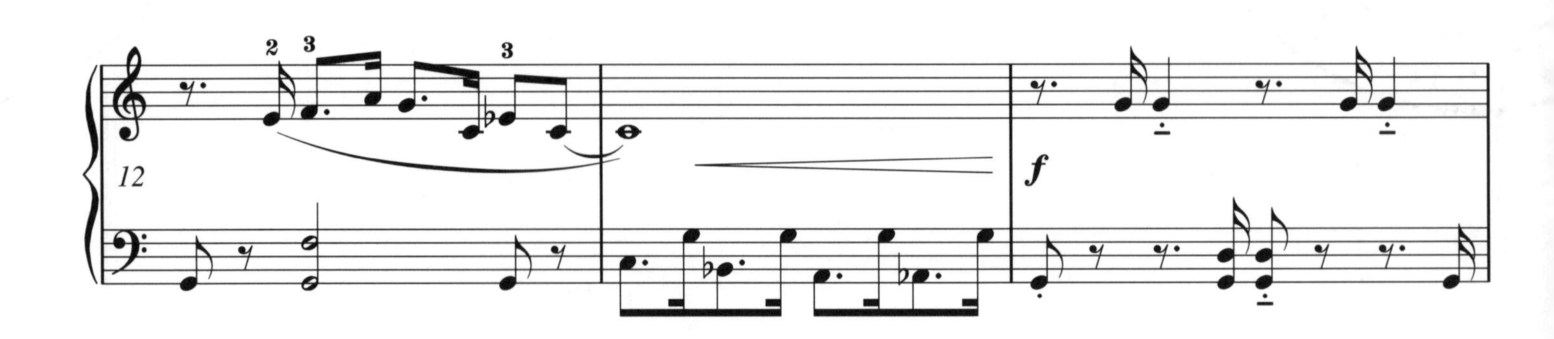

15
18
21
24
mf
f
ff

Cool Customer

13
mp
f

17
mf

21

25
dim.
p
pp

Torch Song

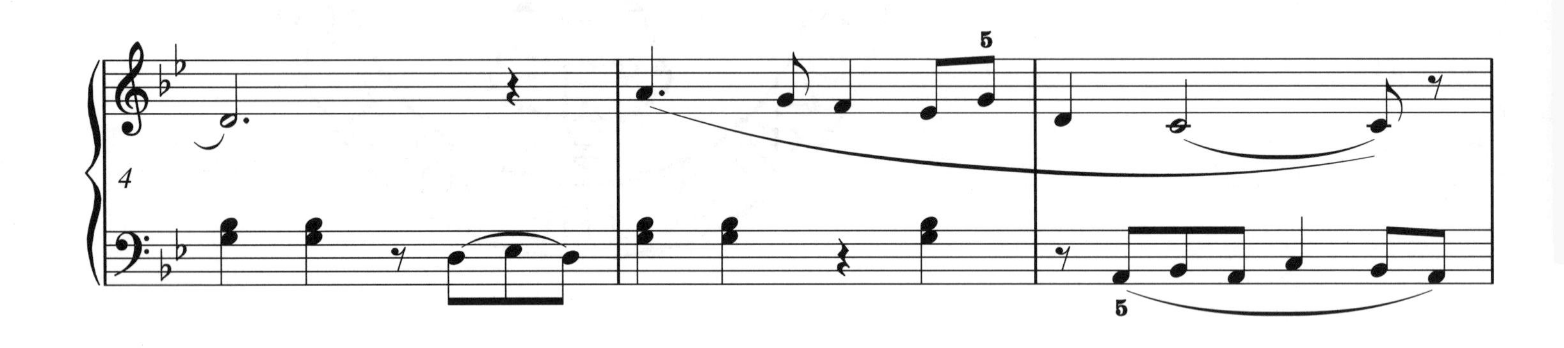

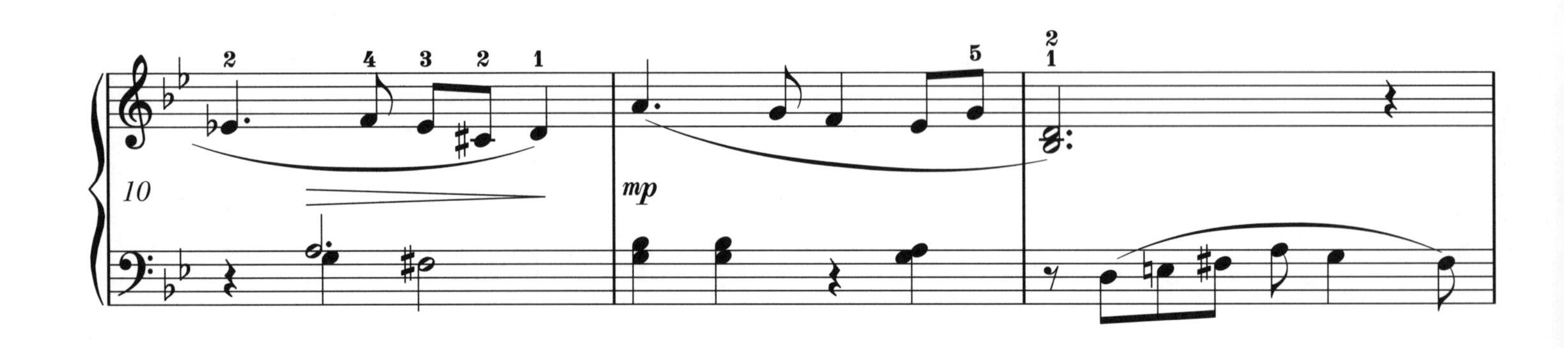

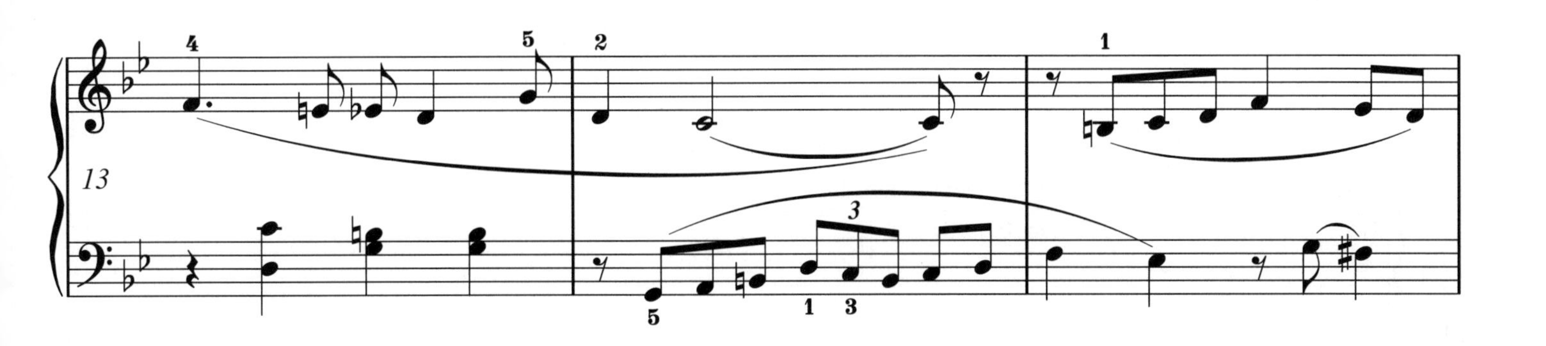
13

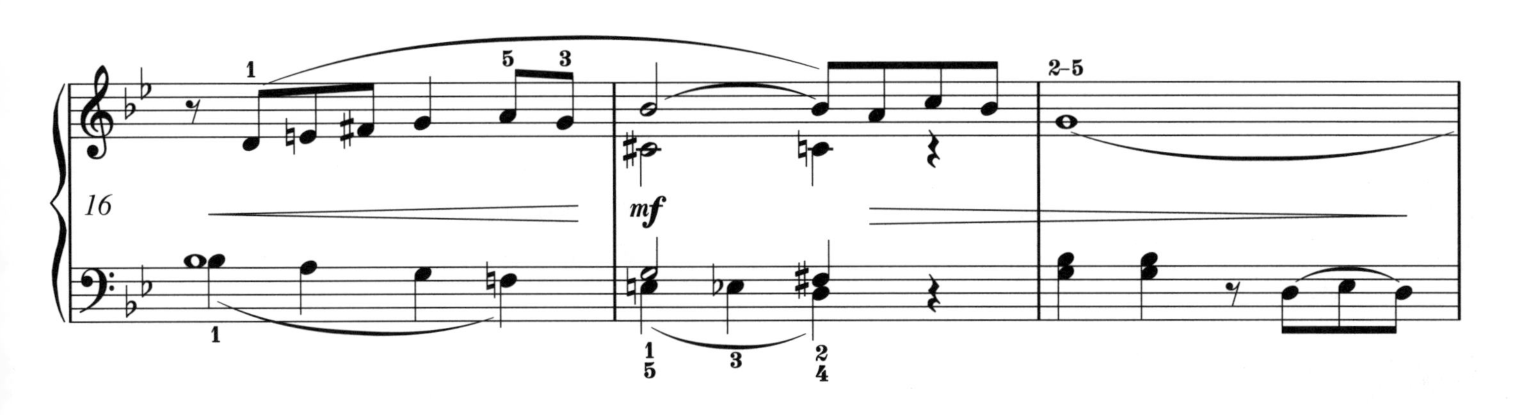
16
mf

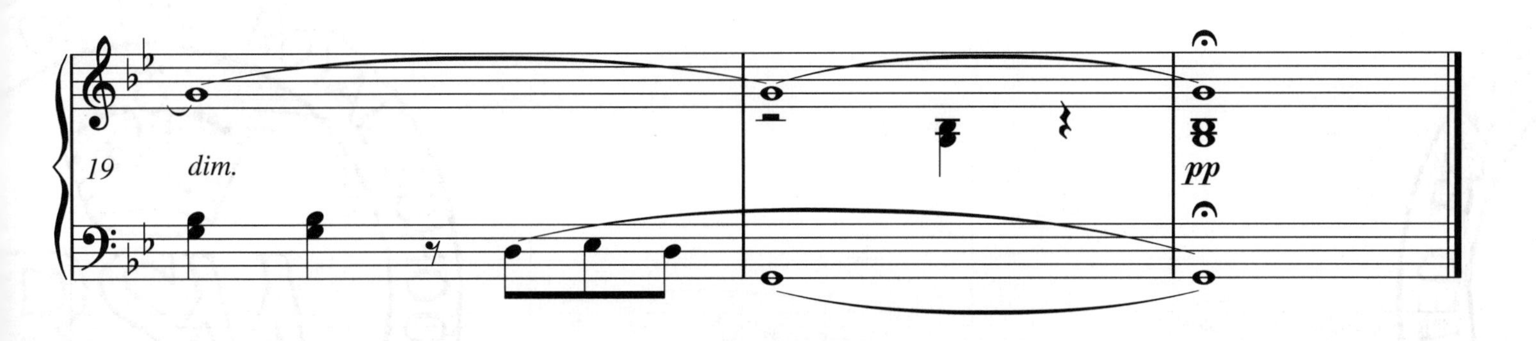
19
dim.
pp

Bygone Beguine

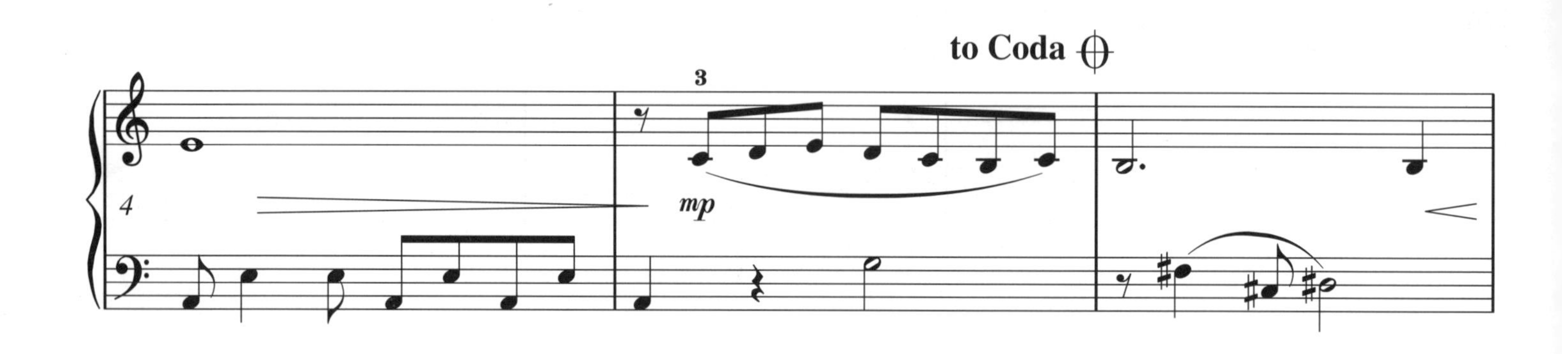

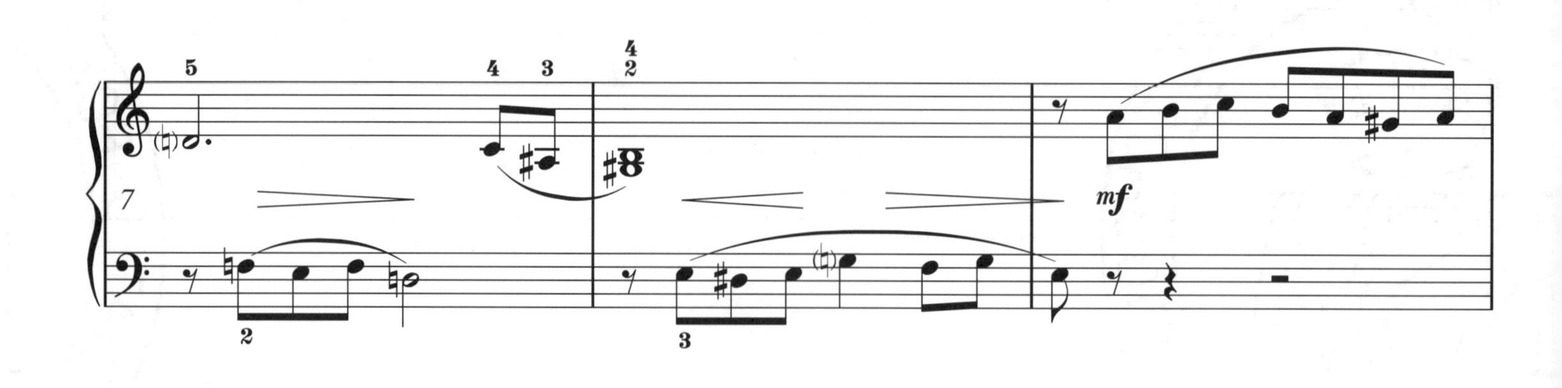

mp
mf
D.S. al Coda
CODA
p

Ragamuffin

2
1
4
3
1
16
mp
2
20
mp
f
1
3
23
2
mp
27
f
CODA
31
mf
f
D.C. al Coda

Courtship of the Dragonfly

Snake Charmer

Daydreams

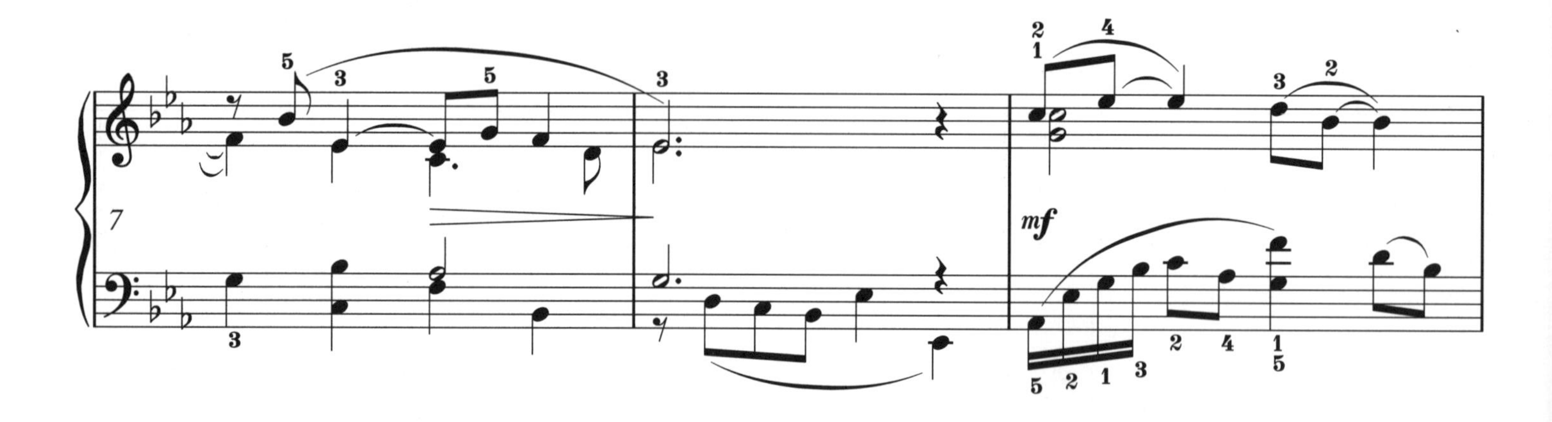

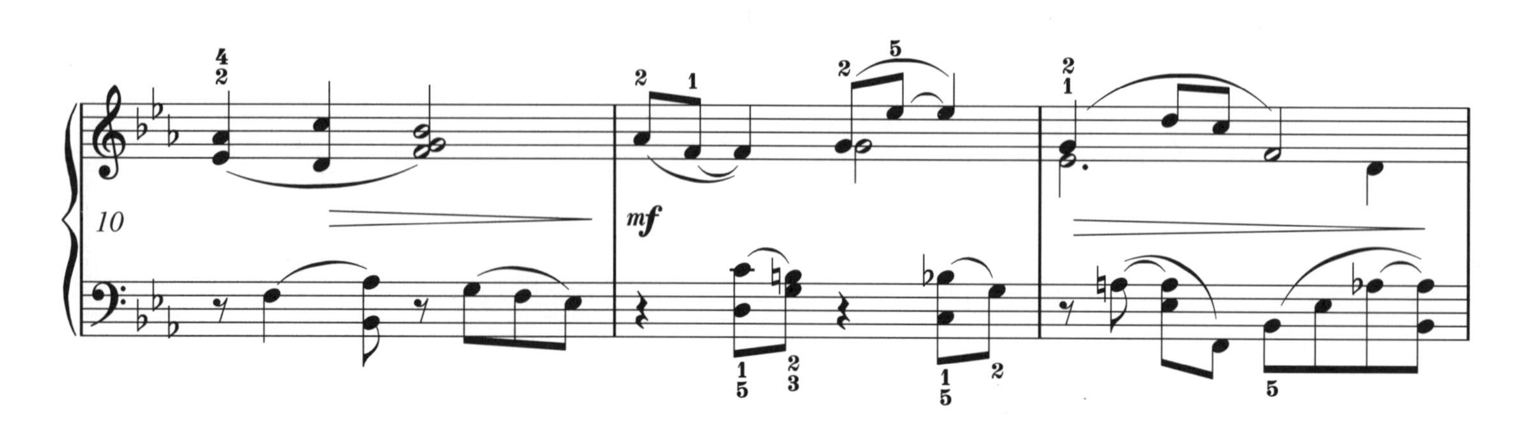

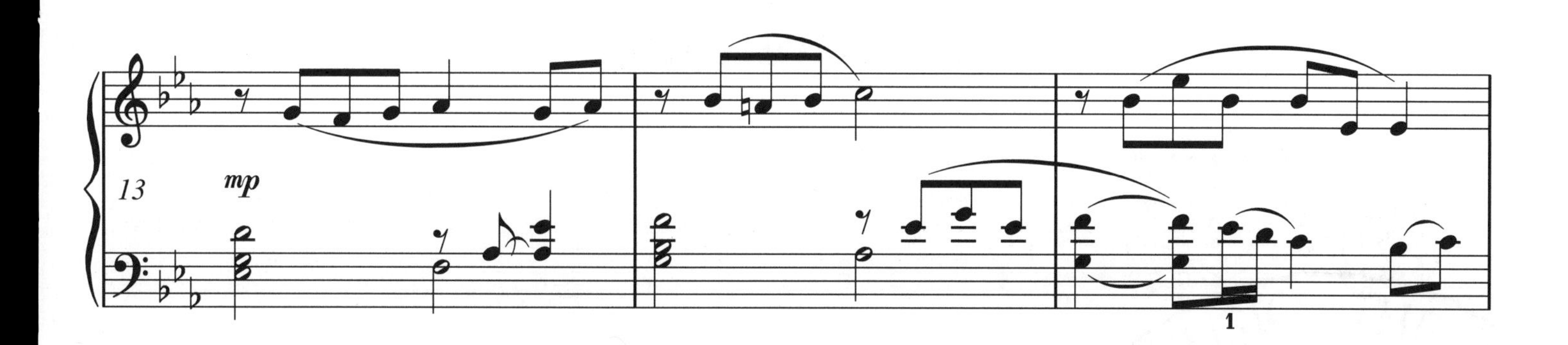
13
mp
1

16
2
1
4

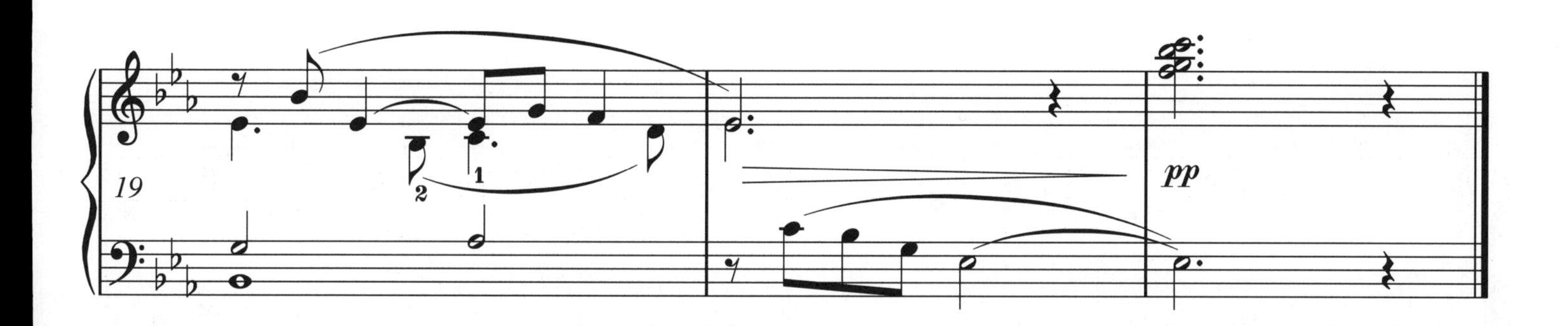
19
2
1
pp

Swingalong

Moderate swing ♩ = *c.*144

10

17
mf
f
21
mf
f
25
mf
f
29
33
p
p
f

Walkin' the Blues

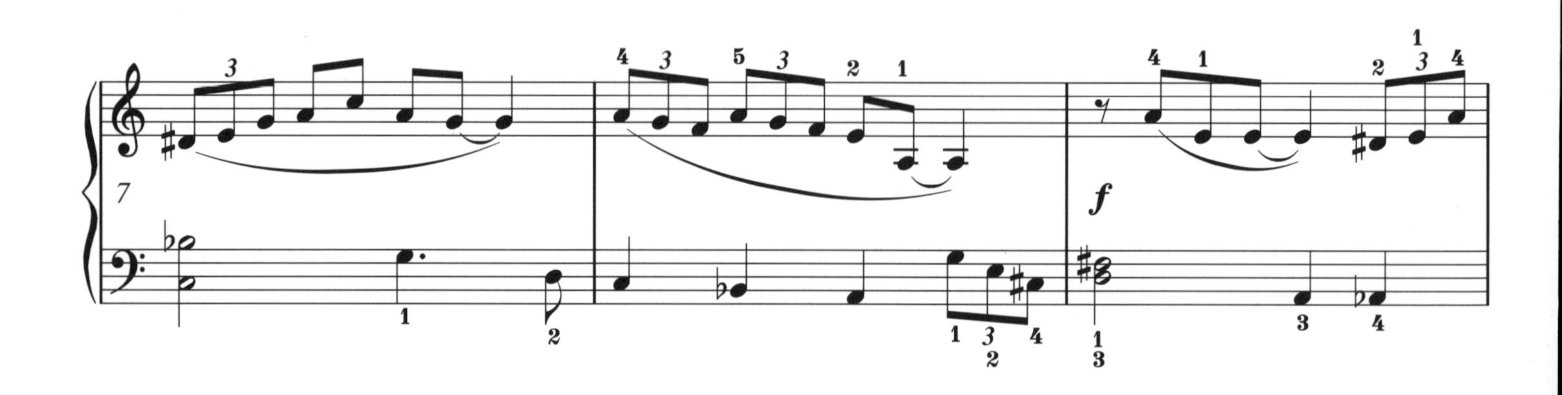

13
mf
16
f
19
mf
22
mp

The Old Meeting Place

With exuberance ♩ = *c.*160 (♫ = ♩♪ triplet)

12

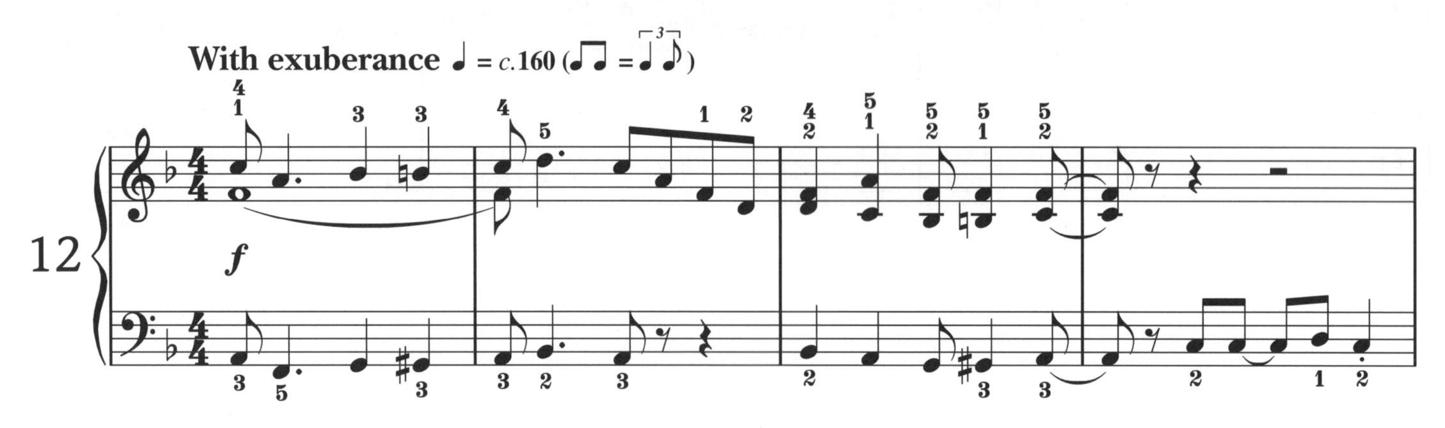

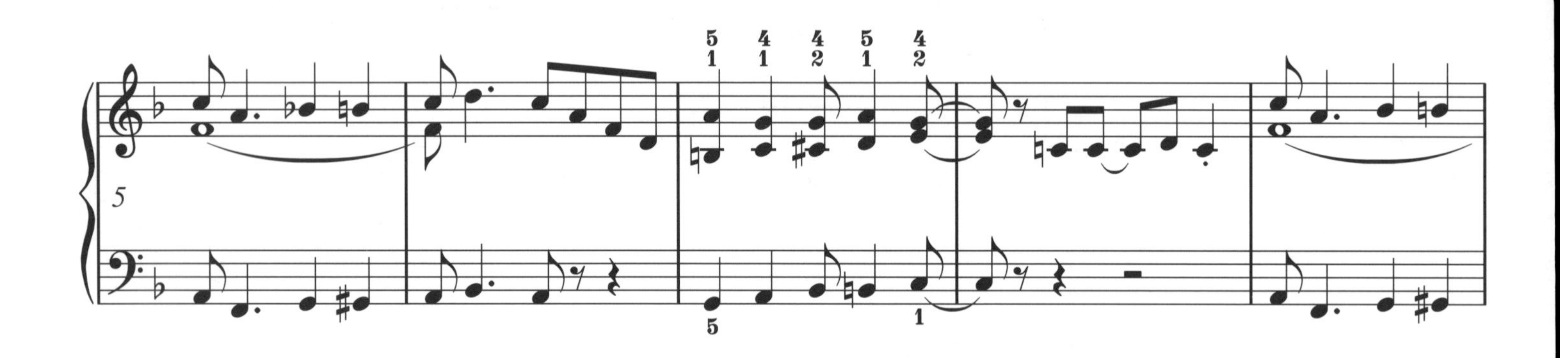

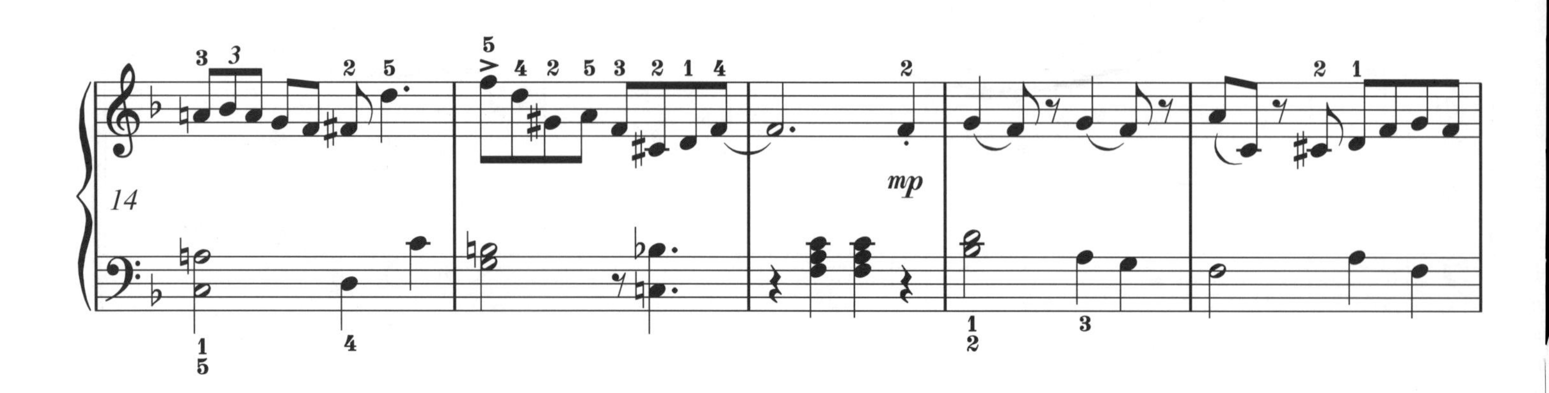

19
23
27
31
CODA
D.C. al Coda
35
mf
ff

Dinner at Eight

Moderate cha-cha ♩ = *c*.126

13

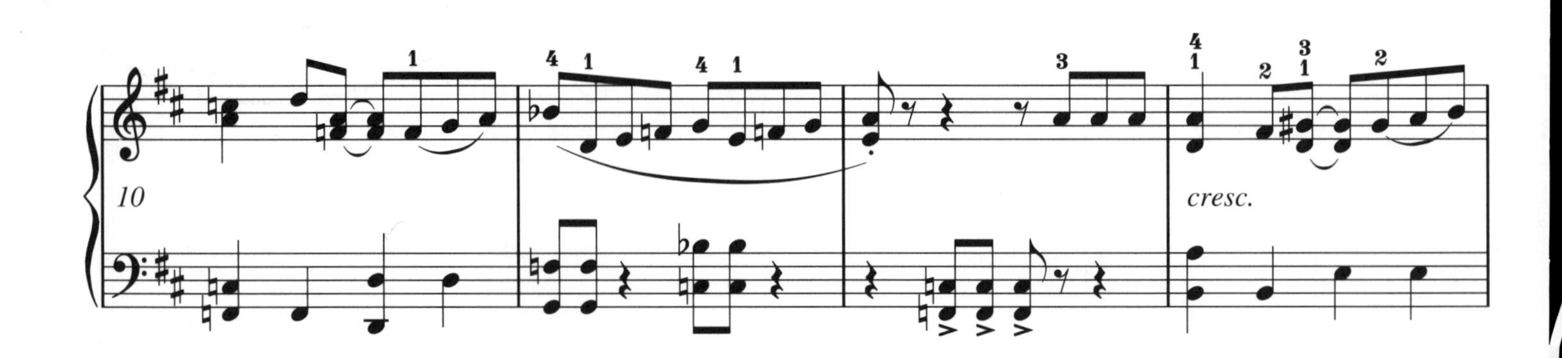

14
f
17
21
25
ff

Canto da Cariri

to Coda
mf
mp
f
D.S. al Coda
CODA
dim. al fine

Holy Roller Coaster

15
ff
f
18
ff
21
f
25
f
29
ff
8

Pease Pudding

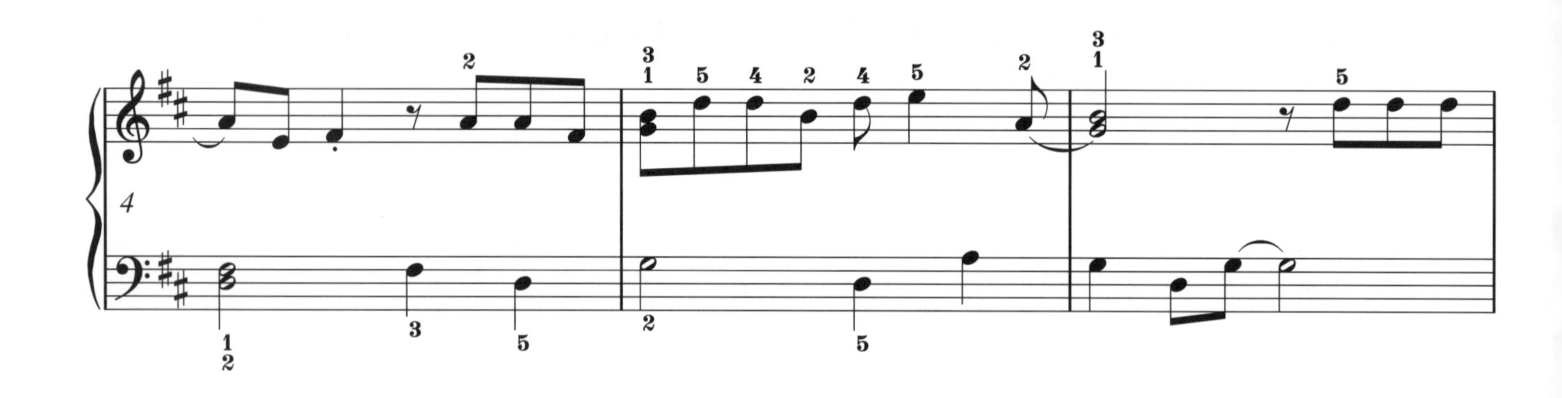

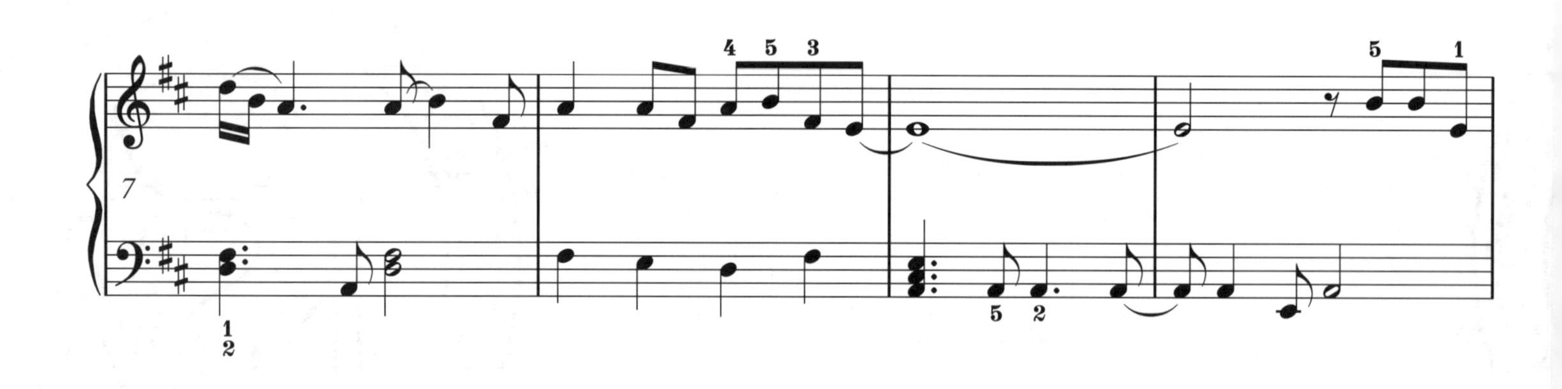

15
ff
19
23
27
28

Stepping Off

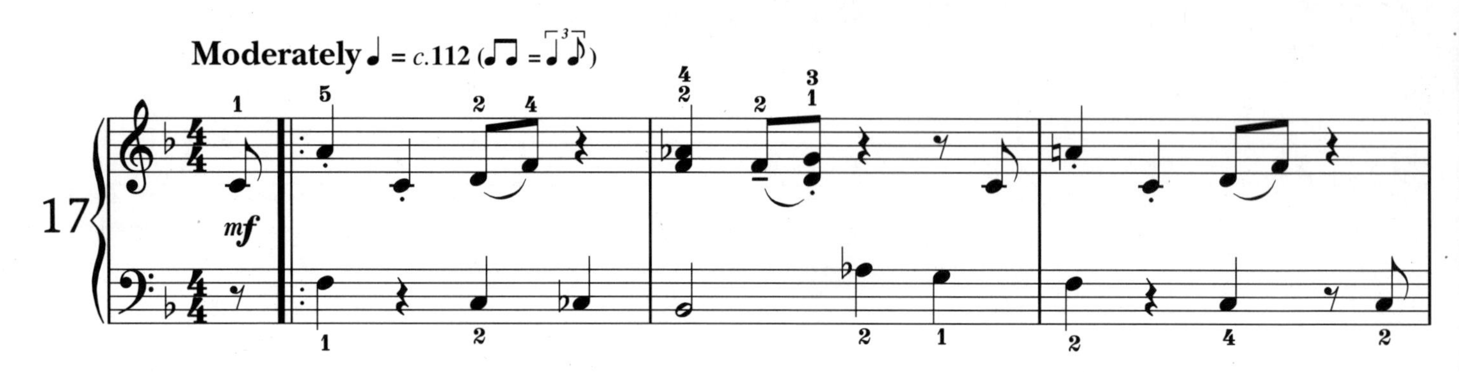

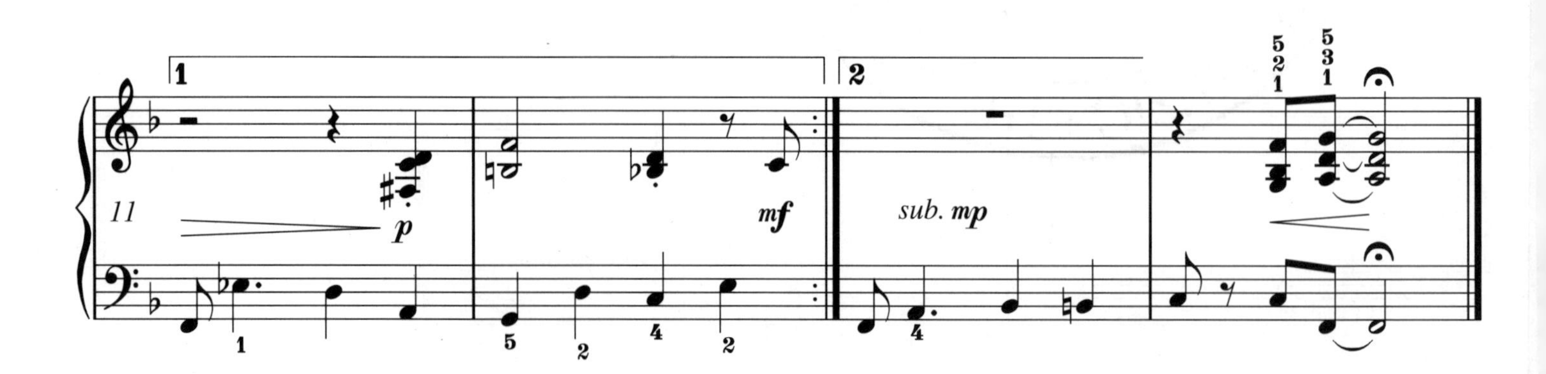

Printed in England by Caligraving Limited Thetford Norfolk

1:01